MR. MEN™ LITTLE MISS™ © THOIP (a SANRIO company)

First published as Mr. Men Trip to the Moon © 2014 THOIP (a SANRIO company)
This edition © 2019 THOIP (a SANRIO company)
Printed and published under licence from Penguin Random House LLC
Published in Great Britain by Egmont UK Limited
The Yellow Building, 1 Nicholas Road, London W11 4AN

ISBN 978 1 4052 9435 5
70396/001
Printed in Great Britain

Photographic image courtesy of Shutterstock.com

Stay safe online. Egmont is not responsible for content hosted by third parties.

Egmont takes its responsibility to the planet and its inhabitants very seriously.
We aim to use paper from well-managed forests run by responsible suppliers.

Later that day he mentioned the idea to Mr Greedy.

Mr Greedy thought it was an excellent plan.

"I hear the moon's made of cheese," he said, licking his lips. "I like cheese."

But Mr Greedy did put Mr Nonsense straight about one thing.

"It's a very long, long way away."

So they went to see Mr Clever.

"What we need is a space rocket," explained Mr Clever. "A space rocket is something I've always wanted to build."

"Will that be very difficult?" asked Mr Nonsense.

"Well, it is rocket science, so the answer is yes," said Mr Clever, who rather likes to show off.

While Mr Clever built the rocket, the other two set about choosing fellow astronauts to travel with them.

Mr Nosey could not go because the space helmet would not fit over his nose.

Mr Tickle and Mr Tall could not go because neither of them could fit into the space suits!

And Little Miss Splendid refused to take off her hat which was no good at all.

Mr Clever had finished the rocket in record time, clever him, and the day of the launch arrived.

"Ten, nine, eight, seven, six, five, four, three, two, one, blast off!" cried Mr Clever, pressing the launch button.

But nothing happened.

Nothing happened because Mr Forgetful had forgotten to fill the fuel tank.

An hour later, the rocket took off, roaring up into the sky trailing a great cloud of smoke.

It rose higher and higher into the air, high above the earth, through the atmosphere and into outer space.

"Oh my!" cried Mr Worry. "I'm floating!"

And so he was.

And so was everyone else.

"We don't weigh so much in space," explained Mr Clever, cleverly. "The air is much thinner up here."

"Unlike Mr Greedy," chipped in Mr Rude, rudely.

It wasn't long before Mr Greedy began to feel hungry, so he cooked spaghetti for everyone.

Perhaps not the most sensible idea!

When they arrived, Mr Nonsense was the first to walk on the moon because it had all been his idea.

Although, he kept an eye out for jumping cows.

It was Mr Worry who discovered strange footprints on the surface of the moon, which he followed, while worrying he was about to bump into a space alien.

He was rather relieved to find it was Little Miss Scary walking on her hands.

Mr Small could not believe it.

He could lift Mr Greedy above his head with one finger!

Everyone had a wonderful day on the moon.

Everyone except for Mr Greedy, who was disappointed to discover that the moon is not made of cheese.

"I told you so," said Mr Clever, something that Mr Clever never tires of saying.

The next day they packed up and went home.

It had been a splendid adventure and Mr Nonsense was very pleased with himself.

And so were all who lived in Nonsenseland.

All except one.

"Go to the moon? What nonsense."

Said the cow!

For Jim Dowson,
a gentle man
N.D.

For Dave and Lucy
J.C.

First published 2004 by Walker Books Ltd
87 Vauxhall Walk, London SE11 5HJ

This edition published 2008

2 4 6 8 10 9 7 5 3 1

Text © 2004 Nick Dowson
Illustrations © 2004 Jane Chapman

The right of Nick Dowson and Jane Chapman to be identified as
author and illustrator respectively of this work has been asserted by
them in accordance with the Copyright, Designs and Patents Act 1988

This book has been typeset in Poliphilus and Caslon Antique

Printed in China

British Library Cataloguing in Publication Data:
a catalogue record for this book is available from the British Library

ISBN 978-1-4063-1296-6

www.walkerbooks.co.uk

Tigress

Nick Dowson

illustrated by Jane Chapman

Twigs with whiskers?

A tree with a tail?

Or is it a tigress,

hiding?

Tigers are rarely seen, even though they can grow as big as Shetland ponies. The tigers' bright stripes are perfect camouflage in their natural surroundings.

She can look exactly like a patch of forest, just by being there.
When she stalks slowly through leaves and shadows,
or crouches still in elephant grass,
her fiery stripy coat seems to vanish
like **magic.**

Bigger than your fist,
her pink nose sniffs the air.

Her ears turn to listen
for the smallest noise.

Bright as torches,
her large yellow eyes
gleam all around.

Tigers don't have a great sense of smell, but their eyesight is six times better than ours, and they have amazing hearing.

8

She's searching for a new den.

Somewhere safe for young cubs.

Smooth as a river she moves;
her plate-sized paws press the ground
but don't make a sound.
When she runs, strong muscles stretch
and ripple her body like wind on water.

She finds an untidy pile of rocks across the clearing,
full of dark cracks and crevices.
Perfect hiding for tiny cubs.

She will bring them here tonight.

Mother tigers look after their cubs alone;
so when the mothers hunt, the cubs are left unprotected.
Changing dens helps to fool predators like leopards
or wild dogs, who may kill the cubs.

Back at the old den the cubs are snuggled deep in shaded sleep.

Their bright white ear spots wink out like magic eyes.

With rough, wet licks from her long tongue, the tigress stirs them awake.

No one knows for sure why tigers have ear spots.
They may help small cubs to follow their mother.
Or perhaps they are flashed as
a warning to other tigers.

Grooming keeps their fur sleek and clean, but the wriggling cubs are eager to feed.
Small as a sugar bag at birth, baby tigers drink rich mother's milk
and fill up like fat, furry cushions.

13

These two are too small to walk far, so the tigress uses tooth-power.

The gentle mother carries her dangling cubs, one by one,

to safety at the new den.

Tiger cubs have loose skin
on their necks, which makes
them easy to lift.

While the tigress hunts for food,
brother and sister stalk,
stretch and snarl.
Teeth bared, heads together,

this could be a tiger fight.

But their knife-sharp claws are
sheathed this time, and don't draw
blood. The cubs are six months
old now – when they are
older their claws will cut
deep into the hardest wood,
or the tough hide of
their prey.

Tigers can get badly hurt in fights,
so they usually avoid each other. Tigers
find their own territory, which they mark
by scratching trees and rocks and by leaving
their scent on bushes and leaves.

Sharp grass stems scratch three empty bellies.
For days mother and cubs have chewed old
skin and crunched cold bones.
The tigress needs a big kill, and now
the hungry year-old cubs are too big
and strong to play-hunt by the den.

A wild pig's big, bristly head bends
as his snout shoves and snuffles for grubs.
Fierce eyes burning, noses wrinkling
with his smell, the three tigers creep
closer with soft, slow steps
and crouch, still as stone.

Young tigers start eating
meat at around eight weeks old.
They start hunting when they are half-grown.

The cubs' whiskers quiver. Their hearts thump loud as drums.
Like fire the roaring tigress leaps and falls
in a crush of teeth and muscle,
and, mouths open, her snarling
cubs rush in.

Tigers are good hunters, but even they only catch their
prey on average three times out of every ten attempts.
Tiger cubs always eat first, and if there's not much
meat the mother may not feed at all.

Now the family will eat its fill.

The sun turns tiger fur oven-hot,
so after the big feed and a sleep,
the tigress heads for the lake.

While her cubs splash and
swim, she floats in cool,
green water to soak
away the heat.

Tigers are among the few big cats
to enjoy swimming.

Between eighteen months and three years old, tigers leave their old territory and find a new territory of their own.

Three sleek tigers prowl the midnight forest.

The tigress taught the two cubs all her tricks.

Now, at eighteen months, they must find their own homes without her.

About the Author

Nick Dowson is a teacher and this is his first book. He has always been interested in tigers. "Tigers are one of the creatures that sometimes roam my dreams," Nick says. "They are completely captivating and remain mysterious. I'd hate to see them pushed off the world."

About the Illustrator

Jane Chapman is the award-winning illustrator of many books, including *The Emperor's Egg* and *One Tiny Turtle*. She thinks that tiger mums have a really tough time in India's climate. "I would be so grumpy in all that heat," she says. "No wonder they spend so much time in the water!"

About Tigers

For years tigers were hunted and killed in large numbers, and of the eight kinds that once prowled the forests, only five survive. There are fewer than 6,000 tigers alive today, scattered across parts of China, Indonesia, India and south-east Russia.

Today tigers are protected, but poachers still kill them; and people want the land where they live, threatening our last wild tigers with total extinction.

Index

camouflage..... 6

claws..... 16

cubs..... 9–15, 16, 18–22, 24

den..... 9, 11–12, 14, 18

ears..... 8, 12–13

ear spots..... 12–13

eating..... 19, 21

eyes..... 8, 18

feeding..... 13, 18, 21, 22

fighting..... 16–17

fur..... 13, 22

grooming..... 13

hiding..... 6, 10

hunting..... 11, 16, 19, 21

nose..... 8, 18

paws..... 10

stalking..... 7, 16

stripes..... 6, 25

swimming..... 22–23

teeth..... 16, 20

territory..... 17, 24

whiskers..... 6, 20

Look up the pages to find out about all these tiger things. Don't forget to look at both kinds of word –

this kind and *this kind.*

She watches the forest swallow his tail.

Then she turns, silently crosses the moonlit clearing.

And, just like her magic mother, the young tigress

vanishes.

A pattern of gliding stripes slides into the trees

and the mother disappears.

Brother nuzzles sister for the last time, and walks away.

Praise for Nature Storybooks...

"For the child who constantly asks How? Why?
and What For? this series is excellent."
The Sunday Express

"A boon to parents seeking non-fiction picture books to read
with their children. They have excellent texts
and a very high standard of illustration to go with them."
The Daily Telegraph

"As books to engage and delight children, they work superbly.
I would certainly want a set in any primary
classroom I was working in."
Times Educational Supplement

"Here are books that stand out from the crowd,
each one real and individual in its own right and
the whole lot as different from most other series non-fiction
as tasty Lancashire is from processed Cheddar."
Books for Keeps

Find notes for teachers about how to use Nature Storybooks in the classroom at
www.walkerbooks.co.uk

Nature Storybooks support KS 1-2 Science

Call the
Ambulance

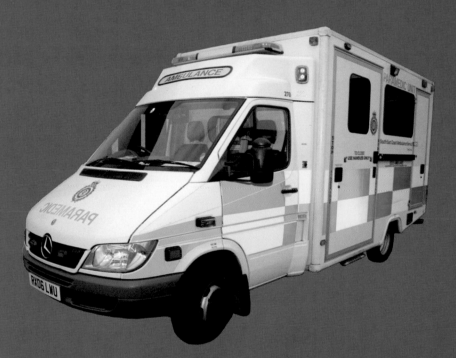

Cath Senker

Photography by Howard Davies

FRANKLIN WATTS
LONDON • SYDNEY

This edition 2013

First published in 2010 by
Franklin Watts
338 Euston Road
London NW1 3BH

Franklin Watts Australia
Level 17/207 Kent Street
Sydney NSW 2000

Copyright © Franklin Watts 2010

Series editor: Julia Bird
Design: Nimbus Design
Photography: Howard Davies

A CIP catalogue record for this book is available
from the British Library.

ISBN 978 1 4451 1736 2

Dewey classification: 362.1'88

Every attempt has been made to clear copyright.
Should there be any inadvertent omission,
please apply to the publisher for rectification.

Printed in China

Franklin Watts is a division of Hachette Children's
Books, an Hachette UK company.
www.hachette.co.uk

Acknowledgements

The author and photographer would like to thank
the following for their help in producing this book:
Denise Anderson; Michael Cardona; Esther Cardona
Senker; Abi, Amalia and Elias Cohen; Joe and Finn
Davies; Michelle and Ricky Gibson; Noah, Heff, Joss and
Isaac Lewes; Naomi Marks; Shelley Noronha; Jacky and
Peter Senker.

We would also like to thank the staff of the ambulance
call centre in Lewes, Sussex; Pat Harrington, Ann
Karura, Fionnula Robinson and East Surrey Hospital
Accident and Emergency Department; Rafal
Kowalczyk, Rich Neocleous and all the crews at
Horsham Ambulance Service; Liz Spiers and David
Wells, South East Coast Ambulance Service; Surrey Air
Ambulance Service.

Special thanks to Helena Saarepera from South East
Coast Ambulance Service.

We would also like to thank Surrey Air Ambulance for
providing the photo on p20.

The photos in this book show members of the
emergency services and models. The names of the
models have been changed to protect their privacy.

Cover image: A paramedic drives an ambulance fast,
but safely, to get to an emergency.

Contents

The ambulance team »   6

At the ambulance station »   8

The ambulance »   10

Inside the ambulance »   12

Training »   14

Rapid response! »   16

Heart attack »   18

Road accident »   20

Emergencies at home »   22

Going to hospital »   24

Keep safe! »   26

Glossary »   28

Finding out more »   29

Index »   30

Words in **bold** can be found in the glossary on page 28.

The ambulance team

If someone is ill or has had an accident, the ambulance team are there to help. A caller dials 999 for the ambulance service. A **control centre** worker takes the call. If it's an **emergency**, an ambulance is called. »

The staff at the control centre check the map and work out which ambulance crew to send out.

>> The ambulance crew arrives as fast as possible. **Ambulance technicians** and **paramedics** know how to save lives. They use medical **equipment** and can give out **oxygen** and medicine. Paramedics are more **senior** workers.

Ambulance crew members at Horsham ambulance station in Sussex.

At the ambulance station

Ambulance workers are on hand 24 hours a day. They work **shifts** – either days or nights. Between calls, they may go back to the ambulance station. At the station, they can have something to eat. They also check the ambulance equipment. »

A member of the ambulance crew checks that the **suction unit** is working.

>> Ambulance workers have to keep up their skills. Sometimes they study together on the computer.

The ambulance

An ambulance is a truck with many special features. »

siren *makes a loud noise to warn people to keep out of the way*

white light helps the crew find the right house in the dark

blue lights flash to warn traffic to get out of the way

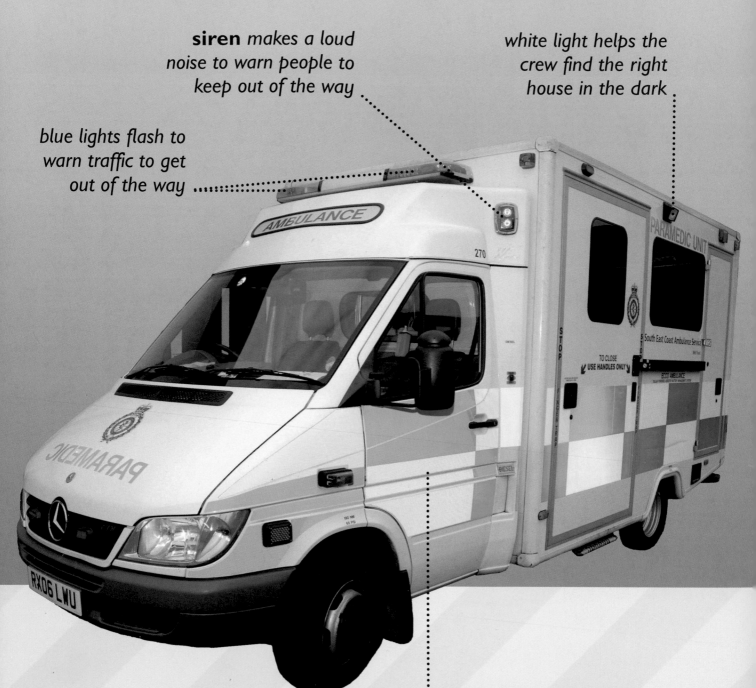

reflective markings make the ambulance easy to spot in the dark

>> There are special features in the driver's cab, too. The crew have a **two-way radio** to speak to the control centre. They can check the address of the emergency on the **sat nav**.

A crew member uses the two-way radio to tell the control centre staff that they are on the way to the hospital.

Inside the ambulance

The ambulance is packed with special medical equipment for treating people in an emergency. »

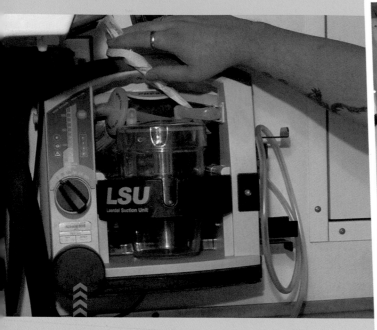

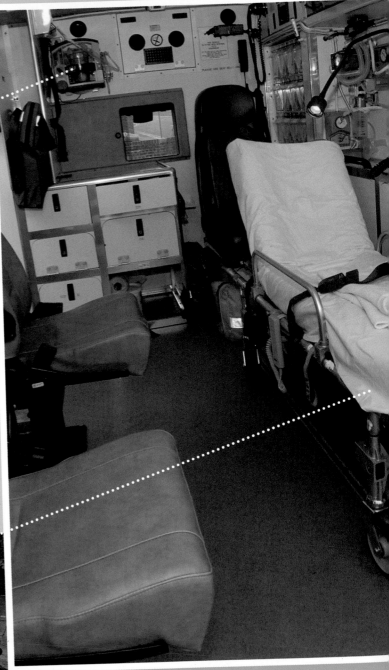

The crew use a suction unit on patients who have something stuck in their throat.

The **stretcher** can be wheeled in and out of the ambulance.

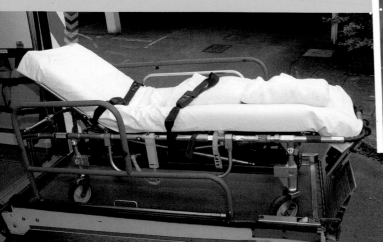

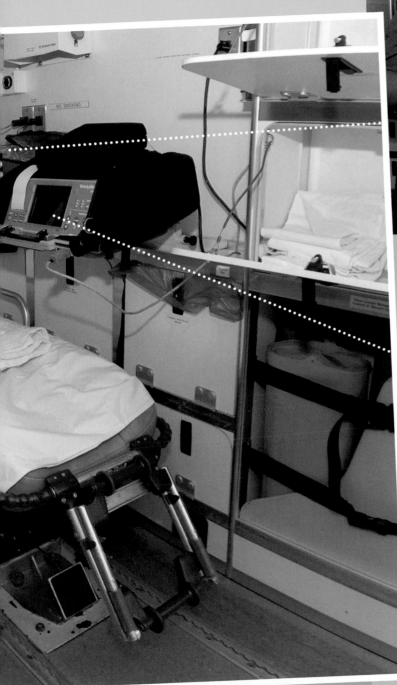

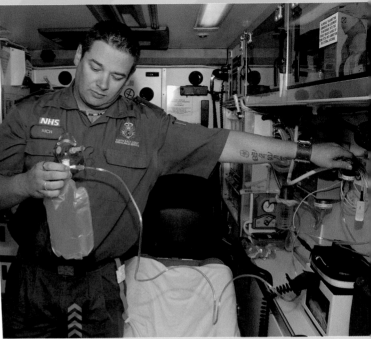

This is an **oxygen unit**. The **mask** goes over the face to help the patient to breathe.

A **defibrillator** or 'shock box' starts a patient's heart again if it has stopped.

Training

To train to be a paramedic, you need to be fit, healthy and strong. It takes at least three years to train for the job.

Student paramedics study the human body, illness and how to make people better. They also learn to drive fast, but safely, in an emergency. **»**

A paramedic shows a student paramedic how to put a patient's arm in a **sling**.

>> To become a paramedic you have to go to university. Student paramedics are taught to work out quickly what has happened to a patient. They learn how to treat people who have had accidents, burns, **heart attacks** and falls.

The crew show the student paramedic how to wrap a patient in a **foil blanket** to keep him warm. She practises placing a mask over his face.

Rapid response!

After picking up a 999 call, the control centre worker calls the ambulance station. A crew of two prepare to leave as quickly as possible. »

The crew stop what they are doing. They hurry into the ambulance within 30 seconds!

Ambulance drivers have special blue light training to learn how to drive safely at high speed.

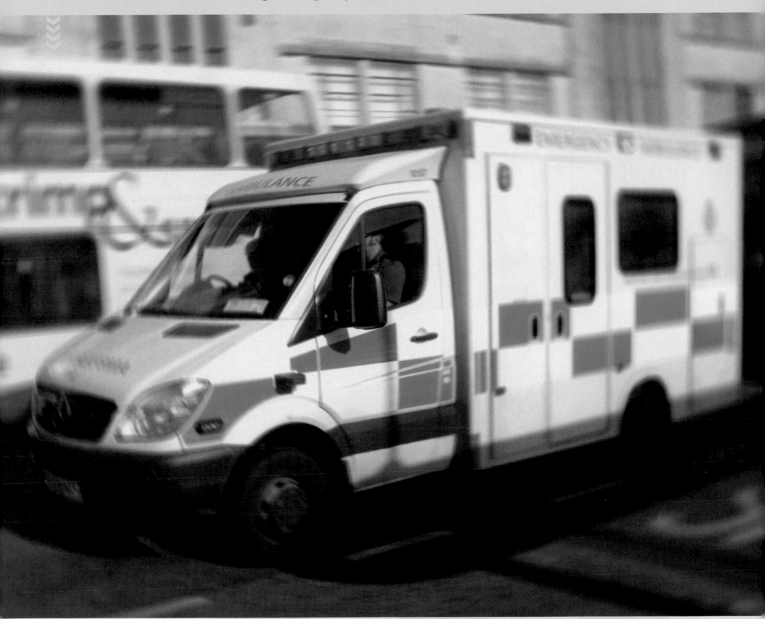

>> The ambulance drives at great speed. The siren blares and the blue lights flash. Cars have to move out of the way to let the ambulance pass.

Heart attack

Sarah has had a heart attack. Her husband calls an ambulance and the crew arrive quickly at the emergency. »

Sarah has had a heart attack in her garden.

» The ambulance crew have to work quickly. If Sarah is not treated straight away, she will die. »

One ambulance worker presses down on
Sarah's chest to keep her heart beating.
The other gets the defibrillator ready.

» They use the defibrillator to give Sarah an
electric shock. It makes her heart start working
again. Then they take her to hospital where she
may have an **operation**.

Road accident

Several cars have crashed in a road accident. The air ambulance has been called. It's quicker to take badly hurt patients to hospital by helicopter than by ambulance. »

Helicopters can travel faster than ambulances so are useful in an emergency.

Jacob is wheeled
into the ambulance
on a stretcher.

>> Jacob was in the accident.
He is not badly hurt, so he
can go in an ordinary
ambulance. The crew put
him on a stretcher to keep
him still in case he has
broken any bones.

Jacob has cut his head.
The ambulance crew
bandage the cut to slow
down the bleeding.

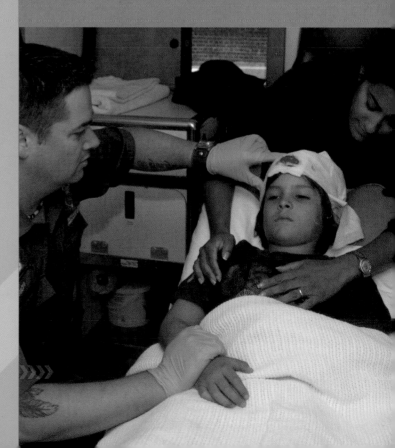

Inside the ambulance, a
crew member checks the
bleeding. Jacob is then
taken to the hospital.

Emergencies at home

Accidents often happen at home. People may fall over. If they are very elderly, they may not be able to get up by themselves.

Sometimes people fall off ladders or chairs while they are working in the house. »

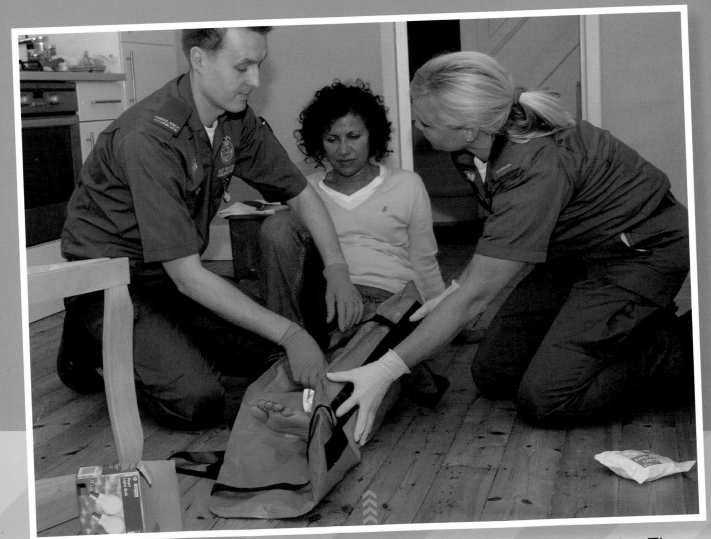

This woman fell and broke her leg. The crew wrap her leg in a **vacuum splint** to keep it still.

>> People with **conditions** such as **asthma** can become very ill at home. Sometimes, they need an ambulance.

Sam usually uses his **inhaler** to treat an asthma attack. If the attack is a bad one, his dad may need to call 999.

>>>>

Going to hospital

Sam's asthma attack is too bad for the inhaler to treat. The paramedics do what they can for him at home. Then they take him to hospital for more treatment. »

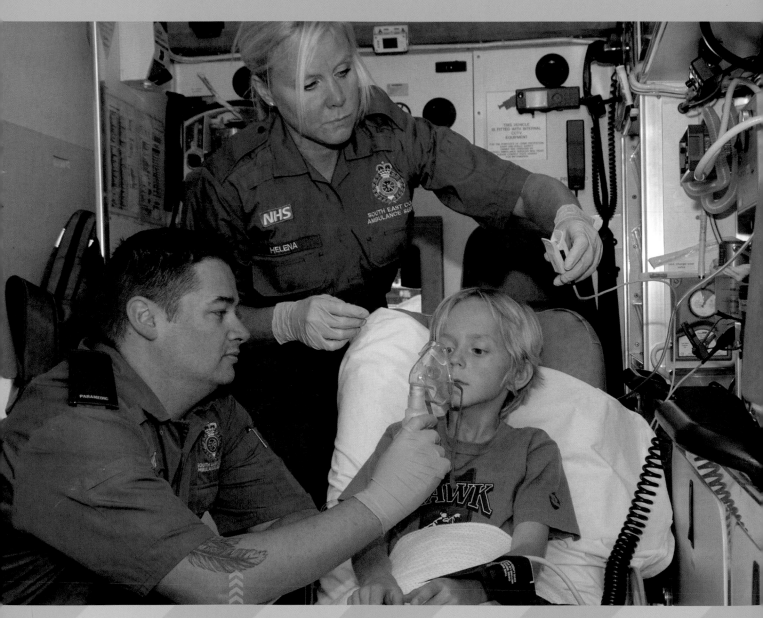

Before leaving for the hospital, the crew place an oxygen mask over Sam's face to help him breathe.

>> The ambulance arrives at hospital. The crew quickly take Sam in on a stretcher. >>

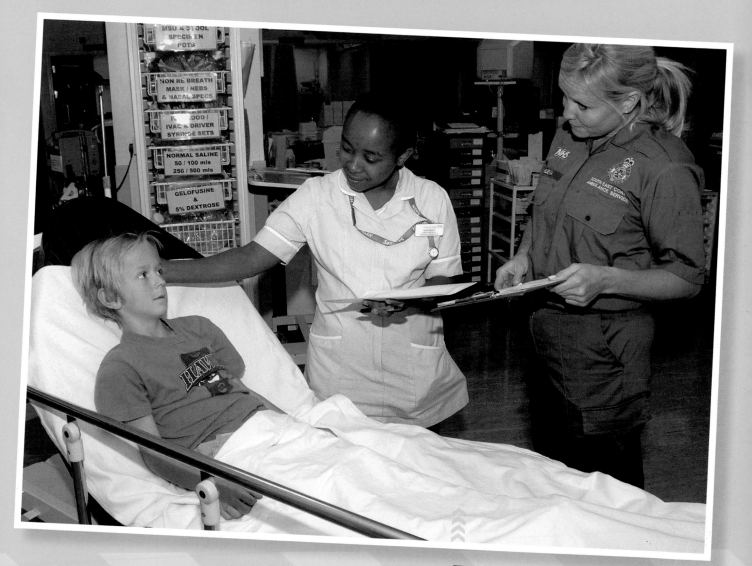

The paramedic explains to the nurse what has happened.

>> A doctor sees Sam and says he will be fine after some more treatment. Sam will be allowed to go home tomorrow.

Keep safe!

You can avoid accidents at home in simple ways.

Be safe with **electricity**. Switch off items like TVs and computers when you're not using them. Make sure people can't trip over the leads. »

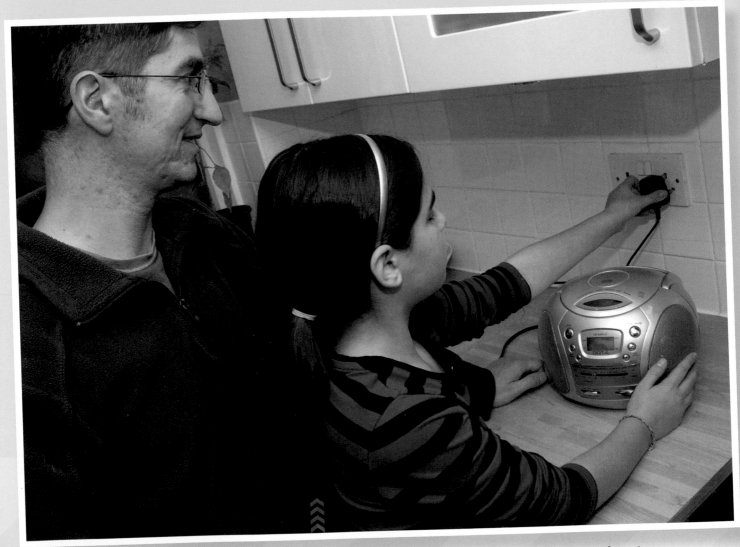

The switch should be off when you plug in a CD player. Plug sockets have electricity in them. Electricity can hurt you. Ask an adult to help you to plug in electrical items.

>> In the kitchen, keep away from the hot cooker and boiling water.

If you're cooking, keep the pan handle to the side. Always ask an adult to help you.

>> Keep safe when you're out and about. Wear a helmet when you go out on your bike or scooter. >>

A cycle helmet protects your head if you fall off.

Glossary

ambulance technician
A person who works with a paramedic. He or she drives the ambulance and helps to save people's lives.

asthma
A condition that makes it hard to breathe.

condition
When something is wrong with your body.

control centre
A place where people take 999 calls.

defibrillator
A machine that gives an electric shock to the heart.

electricity
A form of energy that is used to give power, light and heat. Electricity can be very dangerous if it is not used with care.

emergency
A serious situation that happens suddenly and needs immediate attention.

equipment
Tools and machines that are designed to do a particular job.

foil blanket
A blanket used in an emergency to keep a person warm.

heart attack
Sudden heart disease, when too little blood reaches the heart.

inhaler
A device for breathing in medicine.

operation
When doctors use tools to work on a patient's body.

oxygen
A gas in the air that people need to breathe.

oxygen mask
A mask that covers the nose and mouth and allows you to breathe oxygen.

oxygen unit
A device with a tank of oxygen and a mask for the patient.

paramedic
A senior ambulance worker who uses special equipment to save lives.

sat nav
A device that shows you exactly where you are. It uses a signal from a satellite that orbits (goes around) the Earth.

senior
High in rank.

shift
A shift is the time that a person works, for example, from 7 p.m. to 7 a.m.

siren
A device that makes a loud warning sound.

sling
A bandage hanging from the neck to support a hand or arm.

stretcher
A device like a cot for carrying an injured person.

suction unit
A device that sucks objects or liquid from a person's throat.

two-way radio
A radio for sending and receiving messages.

vacuum splint
A padded wrapping used to protect an injured body part.

Finding out more

Books

Ambulance Crew by Clare Oliver (Franklin Watts, 2007)

Ambulances by Gary M. Amoroso and Cynthia Klingel (Child's World, 2007)

In the Ambulance Service by Ruth Thomson (Wayland, 2008)

Paramedic by Sue Barraclough (Franklin Watts, 2005)

Paramedic by Rebecca Hunter (Cherrytree, 2006)

Websites

British Red Cross Children First Aid
http://childrenfirstaid.redcross.org.uk/
How to carry out emergency first aid – with videos, animations and quizzes.

Children's, Youth and Women's Health Service – Your Health
http://www.cyh.com/HealthTopics/HealthTopicCategories.aspx?p=285
Links to first aid for bleeding, broken bones, burns and people who are badly hurt.

Easy health
http://www.easyhealth.org.uk/callinganambulance.aspx
How to call an ambulance and links to simple information about the health service.

Safe Kids Activities for Kids
http://www.safekids.co.uk/SafetyActivitiesCategory.html
Posters with safety messages to colour in.

Note to parents and teachers: every effort has been made by the Publishers to ensure that these websites are suitable for children, that they are of the highest educational value, and that they contain no inappropriate or offensive material. However, because of the nature of the Internet, it is impossible to guarantee that the contents of these sites will not be altered. We strongly advise that Internet access is supervised by a responsible adult.

Index

A

accidents *6, 15, 20–21, 22, 26, 27*
air ambulance *20*
ambulance crew *6, 7, 8, 10, 11,
    12, 15, 16, 18, 21, 22, 24, 25*
ambulance drivers *17*
ambulance station *7, 8, 16*
ambulance technicians *7, 28*
asthma *23, 24, 28*

B

broken bones *21, 22*

C

control centre *6, 11, 16, 28*

D

defibrillator *13, 19, 28*

E

emergencies *6, 11, 12, 16–17,
    18, 20, 22–23, 28*
equipment *7, 8, 12–13, 28*

F

foil blanket *15, 28*

H

heart attacks *15, 18–19, 28*
hospital *11, 19, 20, 21, 24, 25*

I

inhaler *23, 24, 28*

O

oxygen mask *13, 15, 24, 28*
oxygen unit *13, 28*

P

paramedics *7, 14, 15, 24, 25, 28*

S

safety tips *26–27*
sat nav *11, 28*
siren *10, 17, 28*
sling *14, 28*
stretcher *12, 21, 25, 28*
suction unit *8, 12, 28*

T

two-way radio *11, 28*

V

vacuum splint *22, 28*